*What Do You Say after
You Say You're Sorry?*

What Do You Say after You Say You're Sorry?

How to Visit People in Times of Crisis

Dr. Gene W. Laramy

VANTAGE PRESS
New York / Washington / Atlanta
Los Angeles / Chicago

FIRST EDITION

Copyright © 1985 by Gene W. Laramy

Published by Vantage Press, Inc.
516 West 34th Street, New York, New York 10001

Manufactured in the United States of America
ISBN: 0-533-06454-6

Library of Congress Catalog Card No.: 84-90519

To my wife, INEZ,

without whose love, support,
understanding, and help, this book would
never have been written

CONTENTS

INTRODUCTION

For several months, I conducted workshops on death, dying, grief, and bereavement throughout the southwestern part of the United States. I would open these workshops by asking the participants what they hoped to learn from attending the workshop. Without fail, the participants almost unanimously asked, "What do you say to a dying person?" or "How can you help a person who is bereaved?"

These same questions were asked over and over again during the several years that I served as a parish minister.

When I suggested that I would like to write a book on this subject in order ultimately to help the patient lying in the bed, the majority of the participants urged me to do so.

The purpose of this book, then, is to give clues and help to those who are members of the health care profession as well as anyone who visits people in times of need. It is my hope that through the use of this book, the patient, the patient's family and loved ones, and/or people suffering bereavement and grief will receive the care and attention that is so desperately needed in times of crisis.

The material for this book comes from many sources over many years—books, academic courses, seminars, and workshops—but most of all and more important, from the people with whom I have worked and visited over the years as a parish minister. This is my way of saying thanks for their help in making me a more sensitive, caring person.

What Do You Say after
You Say You're Sorry?

Chapter One

VISITATION—GENERAL RULES

THERE ARE SOME PEOPLE who should never visit people who are in crisis situations. Many times they make the person feel worse. Visiting an ill person, for instance, and dripping woe with every word and facial expression leaves the patient feeling much worse than when you came. On the other hand, entering the room gaily with an affectation of cheer and pretending that nothing is wrong can be just as detrimental because it is false. There is nothing that conveys itself as readily as sincerity in every area of life, so you should always strive to be sincere and honest. It has been said that the basic requirement of all visiting is the ability to *listen*. Some of the values of listening include:

1. Only as a person listens can he or she know what the problems are and how the patient really feels inside.
2. It is through listening that the visitor establishes a relationship and develops a therapeutic rapport.
3. It is when the visitor truly listens that the patient releases emotion, reduces tension, and gives insight into his or her own feelings.

Listening is not easy. It should in no way be confused with passivity. Listening requires complete individual concentration, involvement, and concern, and only as such can be helpful. When one is listening, one should not be doing anything else. Thinking can even be a very active form of doing something. A person should just be open to what is being said and let it soak in.

A good exercise in learning how to listen is to be able to parrot back verbatim what a person has said to you *before* you say a word of your own. Most of the time we find ourselves formulating our own retort or answer to what a person is saying while he or she is speaking and, therefore, we are listening only halfheartedly to what is being said.

A therapeutic relationship grows only as one pours himself or herself into being with the burdened person. This means concentration on *listening, feeling* and *relating*. We cannot, indeed *must* not, assume what another person is feeling. There is no such thing as a general rule for the way people feel about anything. If you are effectively to help the person you are visiting, it will be necessary to understand clearly the patient's inner feelings. Only after establishing that base of operation is it possible to proceed with skill and assurance. One must begin at the hub of the patient's mental, emotional, and spiritual makeup.

When calling on a person, you should be aware of some very important nonverbal communication that serves to indicate where a person is emotionally. Listed below are several examples of nonverbal communication:

1. Physical Indicators
    Moist hands, dry mouth, palpitations of the heart, muscle tension, and/or insomnia usually indicate anxiety.

2. Frequent Body Movements
   Crossing and recrossing one's legs, drumming the fingers, frequent rising from and sitting down in a chair, pacing the floor, increasing intensity of movement, cessation of movement, and biting of fingernails are also indications of anxiety.
3. Voice
   Tenseness, shrillness, rapid speech, stuttering, or pauses in speaking are evidence of anxiety.
4. Mode of Dress
   a. A person who is well dressed and well groomed usually has feelings of security and confidence.
   b. A person who is very strikingly or inappropriately dressed is usually a narcissistic person, often with dependent demands and wishes.
   c. A person who wears flashy clothing and/or exaggerated makeup usually suffers from a poor self-image.
   d. A person who is dressed in a slovenly way and poorly groomed, especially if this is a change from the usual, is usually depressed.
5. Frequent sighing, deep breathing, always being tired, lack of ambition and interest, and slowness of action or speech, if different from the person's normal responses, also indicate depression.
6. If a person sits very close to you, it may indicate fear of rejection or a desire for closeness.
7. If a person sits on the edge of a chair, rigid and upright, it usually indicates tension and anxiety.
8. Laughter
   a. Nervous laughter or inappropriate giggling usually indicates tension and nervousness.
   b. Laughter at inappropriate times indicates maladjustment.

3

c. Free and easy laughter at appropriate times
       indicates good adjustment.

   As you listen in depth with all of your faculties to the multiple levels of communication—verbal and nonverbal—it is good practice to reflect back to the person, in a paraphrased form, what you have heard—particularly the person's dominant feeling—to make sure that you are hearing and perceiving correctly.

   You need to be encouraged to avoid trying to "cure" the person being visited or find "answers" to his or her problems. Instead you should concentrate on trying to understand the person—being with him wherever he is, *not* where you think he should be.

   You should follow these eight steps to encourage emotional release of the person being visited:

   1. Avoid asking informational questions.
   2. Ask about feelings.
   3. Respond to feelings rather than intellectual content.
   4. Watch and listen closely for doors to open and answers that lead to the emotional level of communication.
   5. Be especially alert to negative feelings.
   6. Avoid premature interpretations of why people function or feel certain ways.
   7. Avoid giving advice.
   8. Follow your "gut" reactions, not your intellect.

   Always remember it is much easier to talk too much than it is to talk too little! Let the patient do the talking; it is therapeutic for him to have the opportunity to ventilate.

   Many times the patient will express a considerable amount of anger. Even though this anger may seem to be directed at you, more often than not it is anger at what is happening to the patient. The anger, therefore, is being expressed *through* you, not *at* you. The patient should be encouraged to ventilate this anger to get it outside of himself. You should in no way take it personally.

You should at all times be empathetic. There is a big difference between empathy and sympathy. The difference can be illustrated by the following example: You come to a deep hole in the ground, look down into the hole, and see a person at the bottom. To give him some assistance, you jump into the hole with him. This is sympathy. Empathy is when you see the person in the hole, go and get a rope, throw it into the hole, and pull him out. In sympathy, you become part of the problem—you jump into bed with the patient, so to speak. In empathy, you become part of the solution.

Many times the person being visited will cry. A visitor's adverse reaction to tears or the threat of tears spoils more visits than can be imagined. Tears are terribly threatening to a great many people. Accordingly, many visitors try to keep the person being visited from crying. As a result, all of the visitor's efforts and energy may be used up in that direction and the visit becomes a complete flop.

There is nothing wrong with tears. Tears are a God-given release valve and usually make a person feel better. You should remember that you have done nothing to make the person cry. The patient usually cries because of highly personal reasons. So, when the patient seems close to tears, sit by patiently holding his hand while he cries it out. Sometimes this is not easy, but the dividends are well worth it. After tears, the patient is usually able to talk and share what is bothering him. This is often the time when the conversation becomes more than superficial and deep feelings are brought to the surface. You should, therefore, encourage tears. You should give the patient permission to cry—let him know that it is okay and that you are willing to stand by him in his time of need.

Chapter Two

VISITING A HOSPITAL PATIENT

THERE IS MORE TO physical illness than discomfort and/or pain. An imbalance may be observed in terms of anxiety, uncertainty, doubt, and feelings of rejection. Coupled with this strange new imbalance of body and mind is the patient's need to adjust to hospitalization.

Every person employed by a general hospital has a specific job to do, and each job is distinctively related to the overall purpose of the institution. That purpose (one you should constantly keep in mind) is to promote the welfare of the patient— in other words, to make the patient well as quickly as possible. In order that this purpose may be accomplished, it is necessary for each employee of the hospital to do his/her work in such a manner as to create the least amount of confusion and friction with other jobs and persons involved. Therefore, you should always remember that the hospital personnel are in charge and that you must follow all orders and suggestions being made by these personnel. You should plan visits to the hospital during visiting hours and obey all of the rules and regulations prescribed. You should always remember that the patient's main purpose for being in the hospital is not receiving and communicating with visitors, but receiving professional medical attention and, hopefully, getting well!

Illness can be, and often is, a frustrating experience, causing the sick individual to become unreasonable, sensitive, irritable, hostile, suspicious, and anxious. Therefore, above all, you should be extremely sensitive to the patient's feelings.

Following admission to the hospital, the patient finds himself/herself surrounded by unfamiliar equipment, strange procedures, and strange people. Some patients quickly succeed in adjusting to the "ritual," but there are still the moments of loneliness and impatient watching and waiting. It is during this time that you can be most helpful in restoring the patient's perspective. With quiet calm and in an unhurried but not unduly extended visit, you can bring new hope and confidence to the patient. In order to do this effectively, however, there are some general rules that you should explicitly follow.

Listed below are some very important, but often neglected, mechanical rules to follow when visiting the hospital patient:

1. *Always check at the nurses' station before visiting the patient!*

   One should always stop at the nurses' station before going into the patient's room. The nurse will be able to tell you if, in fact, the patient is feeling up to receiving visitors. The nurse can also give clues as to how the patient is feeling, hints on how to be of help to the patient, and information on whether any new medical paraphernalia has been brought in, if there have been or are other people visiting the patient, et cetera.

2. *Never enter a hospital room when the door is closed!*

   It is good policy in general hospital visiting not to go into any room where the door is closed without finding out something of the circumstances that exist behind the door. The patient could very well be sleeping; the doctor may be with the patient; the nurses may be working with the patient—giving a bath, changing the sheets, changing the medical paraphernalia, changing the patient's postion, or helping the patient on or off the commode. Save yourself some embarrassment—check at the nurses' station; they will be able to help. Remember, most patients, unless they are alseep, critically ill, highly nervous and anxious, or being assisted in some way by the doctor or nurse, like to have their door open or at least partly ajar. Therefore, a good rule of thumb is: if the door is closed, do not enter.

3. *Be careful to note "No Visiting" and "Isolation" signs hanging on the patient's door!*

These signs can be very easily overlooked when the door is partly open. There is a definite reason for the "No Visiting" signs, and they mean exactly what they say. Remember, in the hospital the patient's welfare is the most important aspect.

"Isolation" signs denote the fact that the patient either has an open wound subject to infection or has a communicable disease or is highly susceptible to disease. You should always check at the nurses' station before entering a room with one of these signs hanging on the door. Patients in isolation usually suffer from severe loneliness because they are not allowed any visitors. Therefore, you should ask the nurse if it would be possible to secure a mask and gown so that you could visit the patient for a few minutes. In many cases, the nurses will be happy to oblige.

4. *Do not enter a patient's room when the light above the door is on!*

Before entering a patient's room, you should check to see if the light above the door is on. This light is the patient's "call light." Do not enter the room until the nurse has taken care of the patient's needs. Even if the light is out and the door is partially open, it is good policy not to barge right into the room; knock gently before entering.

5. *Upon entering the patient's room, size up the situation!*

You should try to size up the entire situation at a glance during the process of entering the room. By this means alone, one can determine to a great extent what course the visit should take.

Giving no outward indication of surveying the room, you can notice many things:

a. Evidence of previous visitors. If there are no cards or flowers, the patient may be very lonely and feeling depressed.

b. If the patient is staring at the wall—no television or radio playing, shades drawn—it could mean that he/she is quite depressed.

c. The position of the patient in bed and the presence of special hospital equipment—blood transfusions, glucose, antibiotics—would indicate that the patient may be quite ill. Your approach in such a case certainly would not be the same as if the individual were sitting in a chair enjoying the final stages of convalescence. Try to be fully aware of the situation before you reach the patient's bed.

6. *Do not sit on or touch the patient's bed!*

Som patients cannot stand to have their bed rocked from side to side or moved in any way. When a person doesn't feel well, any movement of the bed seems exaggerated and may even make the patient nauseated. A good policy is to never touch or sit on the patient's bed. Also, you should not use the patient's bed as a depository for your coat, sweater, hat, et cetera. Clothing may very well carry dirt and germs that can contaminate the patient's bedding.

Always watch out for "bed cranks" that may be sticking out from under the bed. If you don't see it, you will not only rock the patient's bed, but you may end up in the next bed with a broken leg.

Be cautious of things spilled on the floor, e.g., water, cards, tissue, et cetera. Stepping on such items can make the floor very slippery, causing you to jar the patient's bed or suffer a bad fall yourself. You must always *be alert!*

7. *Be cautious around medical appliances!*

You must be extremely careful when there are medical appliances e.g., intravenous racks or respirators, attached to the bed or standing next to the bed—especially when they are attached to the patient. *Do not move or adjust these appliances in any way—even if the patient asks you to!*

8. *Let the patient take the lead in shaking hands!*

You should never offer to shake hands with the patient unless the patient makes the first move. Perhaps the patient has just suffered a heart attack and must not move his/her arms at all. If the hand is extended, one should certainly take it, but should handle it gently, returning the pressure with like strength. This is no time to show one's athletic prowess!

9. *Take the proper position while visiting!*

Upon entering the room, take a position, whether sitting or standing, in line with the patient's vision. This enables the patient to have eye contact without shifting position or turning his head.

If the patient is lying flat and the bed is not elevated, it is better to stand in line with his vision. Stand at the side of the bed near the head.

If it is possible to sit by the side of the bed and still have eye contact with the patient, it is preferable to do so. This will help the patient relax, and your visit will seem more personal.

Studies have shown that doctors have called on patients two days in a row for exactly five minutes each time. On the first day, they stood by the bed and talked. The second day they sat down and talked. When the patient was asked the question "Was the doctor in today?," the first day the patient said, "Oh, he flew in and flew out again without saying hardly a word. He surely didn't give me much attention." The second day, when asked, the patient said, "Oh, yes, he was in today and we had a long visit. He wasn't in any hurry, and he answered all of my questions and made me feel just great." Keep in mind, the doctor was there the same length of time—five minutes—each day.

10. *Do not engage in a pathological conference!*

You should not make a habit of sharing your own hospital experiences with the patient. This, in reality, is what we call "getting in bed with the patient." Do not talk against the patient's doctor or tell of things you have heard about others having bad experiences with him. Confidence in one's doctor is a great help in the process of healing.

11. *Help the patient to relax!*

Immediately upon entering the room of the patient, you should seek to put the patient at ease. Sitting by the bedside in a relaxed manner, holding the patient's hand, will help to accomplish this goal.

Emotions are contagious. They are caught and absorbed; therefore, you must strive to be as relaxed as possible. Quick, jerky movements or nervous habits such as twirling a key chain, fiddling with purse handles, wringing one's hands, rattling change in one's pockets, or prancing around the room should be strictly avoided.

12. *Do not carry emotional germs from one room to another!*

When one has listened to a sordid confession or has dealt with any highly charged emotional situation while visiting a patient, it is time well spent to make a stop at the soda fountain or at the chapel for a brief prayer before going to the next patient's room. Remember, your feelings and emotions are contagious.

13. *Beware of negative emotional reactions!*

You should be very cautious not to relate negative emotional reactions through voice, countenance, and/or manner. Often the patient will look worse than expected or will have all kinds of tubes and hoses connected to his/her body. Try very hard not to give a negative reaction to what you see.

Sometimes the patient may be in such a pitiful condition or the odor in the room may be so disagreeable as to make for a very unpleasant visit. Remember, though, that the patient, if conscious, is already humiliated enough by his/her condition and is very much aware of the burden he/she is placing upon others without being reminded about it through the negative reactions of the visitor.

14. *Do not bring food to the patient!*

You should never bring food or candy to a patient unless you have first checked with the patient's nurse. Many patients in the hospital are on some sort of diet—especially following surgery—and the wrong food could make them extremely ill.

15. *Do not adjust the bed or hospital equipment!*

You should not adjust the bed, pillows, or hospital equipment even if the patient asks for it to be done. Perhaps the patient has just had cataract surgery and the bed *must* remain flat. Raising the bed could cause serious consequences. You should either ring for or get the nurse when the patient wishes any adjustment to either the bed or the hospital equipment.

16. *Do not visit the sick when you are sick!*

When a person is not sick enough to be in bed, it is tempting to go on with the daily routine. However, if a person is not feeling well in any way, he/she should refrain from visiting the hospital. Hospitalized patients are usually physically run down and are much more susceptible to all kinds of diseases. A good rule of thumb: when you don't feel well, stay away!

17. *Beware of whispering and speaking in low tones!*

You should never, never whisper or speak in low tones to anyone else in the patient's room or near the room if there is the slightest chance that the patient will see you or hear you. You may very well be talking about something quite innocent, such as what you are going to have for supper or perhaps the weather, but the patient will be sure you are talking about his/her condition and will imagine the worst. This can cause the patient unnecessary anxiety and worry. This rule is true even if the patient seems to be unconscious or in a coma. Many patients who have seemed to be "out of it" have been able to tell about everything that was done or said while they were seemingly nonresponsive.

Hearing is usually the last "sense" to leave a person. There have also been cases where a patient who has been very deaf for many years has regained his/her hearing acuity during times of serious illness and/or the dying process. It is good practice to believe that the patient can hear you at all times. Never discuss the patient's illness in or near the patient's room and never make funeral plans over the patient's bed. Chances are very good that the patient will be able to hear every word you say.

18. *Make the visit short!*

Most patients are in the hospital to rest and get well. Therefore, you should never stay so long that the patient gets tired. Remember, you probably are not the only person who will visit the patient on a given day. A hospital visit should never be for more than five to fifteen minutes at a time.

You should also keep in mind that you are there to visit the patient, not to visit with the other visitors. A group of people visiting together in the patient's room is not only rude but very tiring for the patient. If the patient shows signs of being tired or of getting anxious or restless, it is time to leave.

19. *Leave the room when meals are delivered!*

As a general rule, you should plan hospital visitations during visiting hours and at times other than mealtime. If you happen to be in the patient's room when a meal is delivered, you should excuse yourself and leave the room. Very often the patient will be more interested in visiting than eating at the moment and will insist that you remain longer. However, the patient's attitude toward you may change considerably fifteen minutes later when he attempts to eat cold food. Food and sleep are important factors in the recovery of a sick patient. Your visit should not interfere in any way with either.

20. *No smoking!*

You should never smoke in the patient's room. Even though it may not outwardly bother the patient, it may adversely affect his or her health. Remember, you will leave the patient's room, but the patient must remain in that smoke-filled room after you leave.

21. *Be considerate!*

You should always be considerate of the other patients in the room. You should keep your voice low and never discuss the other patients' illnesses. Again, do not smoke. It may bother the other patients.

22. *Do not try to evangelize or pontificate on your religious views!*

Hospital patients are captive audiences. They cannot walk away from the visitor. Therefore, you should never bore them or needle them into accepting religious points of view other than their own. You are, in a sense, a guest in the "home" of the patient. No matter how sick the patient feels, he or she will feel obligated to pay attention to you. Therefore, make the visit as easy as possible on the patient.

23. *Do not play doctor!*

Patients become upset when visitors begin challenging the treatment they are receiving. You must keep in mind that there are never two cases alike. Comparing the patient's illness with some sickness or surgery that you had several years ago and wondering why the doctor hasn't prescribed the same medicine to the patient is not fair to the doctor or the patient.

You should never, never smuggle in any home remedies or medications. You should visit the patient and refrain from being a diagnostician.

24. *Follow the rules in intensive-care and coronary-care units!*

Rules for visitation in the intensive-care and coronary-care units vary with each hospital. The rules are usually posted by the unit's entrance. Usually only members of the immediate family are allowed to visit and then only for five minutes each hour. Whatever the rules, it is imperative that you follow them explicitly. Always knock and wait for the attending nurse to answer before entering either the ICU or CCU.

When visiting the hospitalized patient, remember the rules and helps stated in chapter 1. It is always best to get the patient to talk—this is very therapeutic. Try to get him to discuss his illness. This, after all, is what is uppermost on his mind. Be sincerely interested and concerned. Being a good listener is very important. Remember the rule: It is much easier to say too much than too little.

Chapter Three

VISITING
THE SURGICAL PATIENT

FOR SOME UNKNOWN REASON, people who are faced with surgery usually, at least from outward appearances, pull themselves together, tighten their self-control, deliberately dull their perception and their feelings, deny danger, stoically accept the inevitable and may even display a feeling of cheerfulness.

You should not be fooled, however, by this seemingly emotional containment. No matter how unperturbed the patient may seem, no matter how self-assured and glib he may act, he is almost certain to be "scared stiff." If the truth were known, he is afraid of the surgical procedure and every aspect of it, afraid of pain, of the anesthesia, of disfigurement, of disability. He is afraid of being helpless, of having his modesty transgressed, of showing fear—afraid of a thousand and one things at the same time. Above all, of course, is the fear of dying. Different from some other things people tend to dread, the dread of surgery is well founded, for all surgery involves risks.

The kind of hold the patient has over this dread, however, makes a big difference to his welfare. Some have a hold that is firm, relatively unshakable, and very useful. Others have a very tenuous hold and need considerable reinforcement.

When there is to be surgery that involves the loss of some part of the body, such as an arm, leg, stomach, breast, or eye, there can be a very dramatic reaction to that loss. Even though the doctor is certain the patient will suffer feelings of loss, many times he may not be fully aware of the serious effects such reactions can cause, both on immediate recovery and on eventual adaption to the loss. Nor may the doctor realize that getting the patient to talk freely about his fears and feelings over the loss may very well prevent an unfavorable outcome.

You can be of great help in diminishing the patient's fears. You can and should encourage the patient to talk about the upcoming surgery, to express any fears that he may have, the anger, gut feelings, and reactions. After accomplishing this, you can then change the subject to more pleasant things and thereby get the patient's mind off the impending surgery. This will diminish the patient's fears and worry and help him face the surgery with a more favorable attitude.

You should never forget the patient's family during the surgical procedure. Time is never longer than when one is waiting for a loved one to come back from surgery. You can help considerably by being with the family, keeping them engaged in conversation about unrelated things, taking them out for coffee, and keeping their minds actively occupied so they will not dwell upon what is taking place with their loved one and all of the things that could happen during surgery. Always give the family encouragement and support. By keeping their minds active, the time their loved one is in surgery will seem to go by more rapidly.

Following surgery, do not spend much time visiting the patient, as he will need rest and nursing care. Just let him know you are there and are concerned about his welfare and then leave. Help the family in any way that you can—taking care of children, providing transportation, fixing meals, et cetera.

Chapter Four

VISITING THE NEW MOTHER

MOST HOSPITALS HAVE special visiting hours for the obstetrics department. Many allow only the husband and other family members to visit. Be sure to check the rules before visiting.

Always check at the nurses' station before visiting a new mother. Find out how the patient is feeling, how the baby is doing, and if there is anything you should be aware of before going to the patient's room. This will prevent making mistakes such as cheerfully entering the room only to find out that the baby has some serious problems or was stillborn.

Following the birth of a child, mothers are often emotionally drained, even to the point of depression. Be sensitive to the mother's feelings. Help her to share where she is emotionally. Be a good listener.

You should not forget the father and the other children. So often they are pushed aside, the mother and the new baby being the center of everyone's attention. This can cause feelings of being unwanted and unneeded, jealousy, and even depression in the father and the other children.

You should not handle the new baby unless asked to by the mother or father. This often causes jealousy and feelings of anxiety in the family. Most new mothers and fathers would like to be left alone, at least for a few days, following the birth of a child.

Be especially sensitive and careful around other patients who may be in the same room as the new mother. They may have had a bad experience with their child or may have fears regarding their new baby. It is also possible that the roommate may have just lost a child or had a deformed or retarded child, or in extreme conditions, when the hospital is overcrowded and they have to use the obstetrics department for nonobstetrics patients, the roommate may be a person who is unable to conceive, is recovering from an abortion, or has just had a particularly traumatic hysterectomy.

Chapter Five

VISITING THE SHUT-INS
AND THE ELDERLY

Blessed are they with a cheery smile
Who stop to chat for a little while.

Blessed are they who make it known
That I'm loved, respected, and not alone.

—Esther Mary Walker
"Beatitudes for Friends of the Aged"

THE SHUT-IN IS ONE whose activity is limited to house, wheel-chair, or bed. Radios and television have done much to break the monotony, but the basic problem remains. An odd dilemma confronts the shut-in. In normal living, there is never sufficient time. The shut-in has time, but many shut-ins find it heavy, slow-moving, and meaningless. Sundays and holidays are the longest and most depressing days for the shut-in and the elderly. While they may have the radio, television, books, and handi-work, they still miss companionship. More than that, they feel that they have lost control of their time and, therefore, the structure for purposeful living.

Visitation of the shut-in is very likely to become "routine calling." Ideally, it should be guided visiting or what might be called disciplined conversation. It should seek to probe the inner thoughts of the shut-in. If there is little reflective thinking, you can often stimulate it by discussing books, ideas, or other articles of interest.

Sometimes you can encourage a shut-in person to use his time constructively, even to the point of rehabilitation. There are now extensive programs in almost all areas for self-education and self-help.

However, with all these efforts there are still a few people who will remain shut-ins; many of these have or could have active minds. Others simply wait out time, finding it tedious and dreadful. Here you should not be content until some meaning in his existence can be found for such a person. Your patience, imagination, and dedication will be tested as at few other places.

Older people often become shut-ins or semi–shut-ins and need special attention. Here again the great problem is time and the meaningfulness of time. With more people having a long life expectancy, this problem will, no doubt, increase. It is not enough to live to advanced years, sickly, disgruntled, or with a sour disposition. Rather, one must strive to live enthusiastically, hopefully, and contentedly. Years are being added to life; it is the visitor's duty to help life to be added to years. Income, health, housing, companionship, attitude, and outlook (psychological and philosophical) are the major problems of senior citizens. You can do little about the first three, but can certainly help in the other areas.

You should strive to assist people to have a positive attitude, to handle their advancing years in more meaningful ways. Unfortunately, our world is wasting one of its greatest resources: the wisdom of its senior citizens. Their insights, wisdom, and leadership should be encouraged. When calling upon the elderly, you should do a lot of listening and a lot of encouraging. Calls upon the elderly are not difficult if a person is willing to be a good listener. Unfortunately, the elderly and the shut-ins are too often neglected. You should strive to have an orderly and planned schedule of calling upon the shut-in and the elderly so that they are not overlooked. Remember, someday if you live long enough, you too will be in their place. It is always advisable when calling on anyone to try to put yourself in his situation and then govern yourself accordingly.

Chapter Six

VISITING THE NURSING-HOME PATIENT

NO PEOPLE IN OUR SOCIETY are more neglected as a whole than nursing-home patients. To a patient cut off from the rest of the world, even a well-meaning but tongue-tied and nervous visitor is welcome. All one has to do to be welcome and of help is try to understand these people we call senior citizens. Understanding brings sympathy; sympathy produces empathy, which is the key to real communication. For when we feel with a person, we are truly listening to him and are free to speak.

For instance, it helps to realize that some older folks often tend to be childish. They have no perspective on the future, which is probably why they dwell on the past and a period more real and certain to them. Since they have finished their parental responsibilities, their circle of family and friends diminishes so that they become increasingly self-centered. However, as is also true of children, little things please them: an autumn leaf, a rose, an inexpensive gift, a pretty card, something that you have made, a simple memento of your visit. Similarly, they are easily upset by things that may seem petty to others.

Another characteristic of some older adults is that they are easily confused and easily taken advantage of—one reason they often must live in the protective atmosphere of an institution. It is both unfair and unkind to argue with them or to try to persuade them to your religious or political views. As a visitor, don't try to convert; rather befriend. If someone seeks to hear of your faith, which many patients will, share it; but don't try to impose your particular doctrinal beliefs upon a patient.

Possibly the most difficult side of aging is the problem of communicating. Some can't hear or see well, while others can't talk or talk haltingly. Still others have lost even the ability to respond with facial expressions. Even though they cannot respond, you may rest assured that they are happy you came to visit.

As a group and as individuals, the elderly are often shut off from the rest of the world, castoffs from the busy mainstream of society. No wonder they feel forgotten and neglected though they may be recipients of excellent care in a nursing home. The staff, television, and occasional visitors are their only links with the outside world. By coming, you show them—nor does it hurt to say it as well—that you care about them, that it matters to you that they are lonely. This is why even a brief visit brightens their day. Think of how you enjoy drop-in visitors, whether good friends or, if you are lonely enough, even salespeople. How much more meaningful such moments are to those who actually are often forgotten by friends and even family or who have no one to remember them.

It would be a mistake to stereotype the aged, for they are individuals and distinct personalities, and none of the generalizations that I have mentioned here is true of all the elderly. Through their lifetime they have built up likes and dislikes, fears, and hopes. Some personalities get worse with age; others improve. For every crotchety pessimist, one will find someone else who is optimistic, adaptable, unassuming, charitable, and thoughtful.

Within all older people is the strong need to be of value, to know that it matters to someone that they still inhabit this earth. But, unfortunately, not all do matter to someone, which is why it is so important that you visit.

But what can you do? It pays to give thought to this question before leaving your own home. Just what is it that you wish to accomplish? What specifically can you do once you get there? Your object clearly is to cheer them up, but how?

It may seem obvious, but the greatest thing you can do is simply visit them. They will have the pleasure of seeing someone younger, someone from the outside, and hearing a different voice and seeing a different face. They appreciate any attention you can give, any attempt, however little, at kindness. It is easy for them to feel that those who care for them do so because they are paid to care. It means a lot when someone volunteers a chunk of time for the elderly person's sake. As mentioned before about visiting, keep visits short, but go as frequently as you can.

Another simple but basic instruction is, be complimentary. Even in casual contact, watch for things to praise: hairdo, shawl, room, handiwork, et cetera. Don't push, don't overdo or be insincere, but be alert to opportunities to point out the good. Sometimes a word of appreciation for those who take care of them helps them to see that they are well cared for and loved.

Equally simple, but much harder to follow, is an admonition to be patient. If someone wants to harangue, listen. If you can't rechannel a sob story into a more positive conversation, hear them out. If they speak slowly and/or haltingly, give the impression that you have all the time in the world. This does not mean, however, that you should take seriously everything you hear. A patient may insist that he is being detained against his will—that he is mistreated, that everyone hates him and is against him. You need not agree, but it will do him good to get it off his chest.

Finally, don't hesitate to bring your talents with you and use them, talents such as:

1. The ability to talk with strangers. This improves with practice, and conversation will naturally be easier on subsequent visits to the same person.
2. Reading aloud: the Bible, an inspirational poem, the newspaper. Read what they wish to hear. If you don't know what that might be, ask. Perhaps they would like you to read and reread cards or mail that they have received.
3. Playing the piano or another instrument, singing, et cetera. Of course, be alert. If someone is watching television in the lounge, don't stride in and compete with a piano concert. If the lounge is relatively free, however, you can spread the word of a hymn-sing or private recital—which may not remain private for long.
4. Writing. Offering to write letters that they dictate or perhaps composing simple notes they would like to send. Then take care of mailing these notes for the patient.
5. Personal grooming. How much attention is paid to this by the staff varies from place to place. Some patients really appreciate a manicure or a hair set or a makeup job if you are skilled in the area.
6. A hobby or special interest: gardening, for instance, or houseplants, a postcard or button collection, et cetera. Don't bring your whole collection, but if possible have a sample ready in case you find a

like-minded individual. Old coins or stamps may launch even one who is not a collector into a nostalgic recital of "the good ol' days."

7. A camera. Take a roll of impromptu pictures, have it developed, and either post them on a bulletin board or give them to the person photographed. An Instamatic camera is great for this.

8. A car. With prior permission from the staff, offer to take the patient someplace he or she would like to go. Getting out on a brief shopping jaunt perhaps or to visit his or her old neighbors and friends, to the park, out to lunch or dinner, or simply for a ride to enjoy a beautiful day can serve as a marvelous tonic.

9. Have you any flowers growing in your yard? When spring bushes blossom, pick small bouquets of lilacs or mock orange, for instance, and give a gift of fragrance. Or get the jump on spring and bring in stalks of pussywillow. In the summer, gather cut flowers or distribute rosebuds.

10. Do you like to play games? Bring them along and offer to play with anyone who is interested. Bingo, chess, checkers, and Chinese checkers are favorites.

11. Handicrafts are a promising two-way street. Share your skills or let one of the patients teach you how to knit or crochet. Some nursing homes have handicrafts in their therapy programs; you may be able to work within their framework. If not, you may be able to start something of this nature. One caution! Do not start a program if you won't or can't see it through.

12. We don't usually think of children as talents, but some children (and/or youth) would be marvelous to take along on such a visit. Check before you go to be sure it's permissible to bring a youngster and

be sure to prepare the child on what to expect. Older people always appreciate seeing and holding a baby. You may find yourself drafting a substitute grandparent or a whole bunch of them.

13. If the nursing home allows it, take along a puppy or a kitten. You will be surprised at the response you receive.

To be sure, there are other talents that can be shared. Only you know what lies within your grasp to offer. Examine your assets and give thought to the characteristics of those you are to visit. Then set your feet to walking. Many lonely people are awaiting your coming.

Many people who become residents in a nursing home suffer from confusion and a sense of unreality. It is extremely important that these people are visited often and that the visits consist of reality orientation. Listed below are some ways the visitor can assist in this orientation:

1. Call the nursing-home resident frequently by name. Tell him/her who you are. Don't say, "Do you know who this is?" or "Guess who came to see you today?" Such things will only cause more confusion.
2. Talk about the time and the place where he/she is. Don't say, "Do you know what day of the week this is?" or "Do you know where you are?"
3. Bring in a family photograph and other important photos. You and others can talk to the patient about them.
4. Talk about the season, weather, food, jewelry, flowers, animals, crops, et cetera.
5. Bring objects that can be touched and/or smelled. Colors are important; studies show that blue and red are most preferred.

6. Often older people like to reminisce about events of the past. One reason for this is because short-term memory recall ability is adversely affected by the aging process. An important reason, however, is that the past with all of its experiences needs to be reflected upon and put into perspective by the aged. Reminiscing is a positive experience.

7. The amount of time you spend visiting is less important than how that time is spent. Don't feel guilty if you don't have long visits. Try to make your visits stimulating while you are there.

8. People need a meaning to life in order to live. You should help the resident retain or acquire a meaning to his or her living.

9. Entice the imagination. Most elderly people have a very interesting history. Bring in a tape recorder and a list of questions and help encourage them to record their life history.

10. If the resident doesn't respond appropriately, that's okay. You were there—that is what is felt and is important.

11. If the resident is confused, use short, easy sentences. Don't give more than one instruction at a time. Don't ask more than one question at a time. Give time for a response. Use a quiet and unhurried manner. Sit face to face.

12. Touch is a universal language. Do not hesitate to hold hands or embrace.

13. Be sensitive to the resident's feelings. Remember, care is more important than cure.

Only in a monologue does one have complete control over the subject matter. But in a conversation, you work with what the other person wants to contribute. Thus you might find yourself discussing things you would much prefer not to discuss, with very little you can do about the situation. However, if you do initiate the conversation, you may have some control over its duration. Try to keep the conversation on a positive note. Many elderly people become extremely negative and pessimistic.

What is there to talk about? Some okay topics would include:

1. The patient's family. Usually a patient's family—children, grandchildren, great-grandchildren—are very important to him and he is always ready to share the latest news about them.

2. Your family and your world. Don't immediately launch into a recital of me-my-mine to a total stranger or even to a friend until he has had the opportunity to share the latest news of his family. But when the conversation warms up, don't hesitate to tell personal things about yourself—the ages and antics of your children, amusing family anecdotes, tales of your pets. Share experiences you have had, places you've been, things you've seen, books you've read, and music you like. If you are a farmer, tell of this year's crops or any new animals recently born or added. Don't hesitate to tell of some humorous thing that has happened to you. As you share yourself with the patient, a bond of friendship is created in which he will be able to share some of his deep feelings.

3. The weather is always a good topic because there isn't anything anybody can do about it. Bring this up especially if there is anything unusual about it.

4. Talk about the patient's surroundings and/or personal appearance. Always try to be complimentary.
5. You can usually get a conversation going if you mention former times. All you have to do is lead with the statement "I'll bet you remember when . . . " This is also true with former places that the patient has lived.
6. Enlarge upon the patient's interests as he discloses them. If he is so inclined, let him tell you things.

Some topics should be avoided if possible. These would include death and dying, illness and ailments, fine points of religion, doctrines, interpretation of Scripture, and politics. However, if this seems to be a dire need of the patient, then become a good listener and let him unload. The state of world affairs should be avoided if possible, as this is usually approached in a negative manner. One should try to avoid too much conversation about a patient's health, as this too is usually looked upon in a negative way.

A general rule of thumb when calling upon the nursing-home patient is to be open, honest, cheerful, and positive.

Chapter Seven

VISITING
THE TERMINALLY ILL

DIFFICULTY IN VISITATION TECHNIQUES is nearly always encountered when visiting the dying patient or one who has a life-threatening illness. Part of this difficulty rests with the patient, but a very large part rests with the visitor.

The dying patient is usually one of the loneliest people in the world. No one can die for another person. No one can join another person in the dying process. The patient must go down that trail by himself. Unfortunately, at a time when the dying person needs people around him the most, he receives the least attention. Studies have shown that doctors, nurses, friends, and relatives call on the dying patient the least of all patients in the hospital. The dying patient is usually put in the "last room down the hall" so nurses and doctors won't have to pass by the door as they make their rounds. This makes the patient not only lonely but also have feelings of being unclean or contagious that add considerably to his discomfort. The dying have generally been abandoned and discriminated against long before they are dead, and we who have abandoned them have done so many times without even being aware of it. We actually believe ourselves when we say we don't have time or when we claim to "forget" our dying friends. The dying patient should not be treated as if he is already dead. He should be visited, sat with, talked with, cried with, and listened to. We must realize that patients—including dying patients—are people and continue to be people until the very end. People live by meaning. Any act or attitude that fails to share the quest for meaning—even in the tragic events such as death—is a denial of relationships that cannot be easily accepted. The goals, therefore, when visiting the dying patient are to strengthen the meaning of life. This may even restore life. But, if not, it certainly makes for a richer meaning during the terminal events. The patient, even in the face of death, can rise to the full stature of his being as a person.

When calling upon the terminally ill, you should be aware of the five stages of dying as postulated by Dr. Elisabeth Kubler-Ross in her book *On Death and Dying.** All dying patients do not go through all of the five stages. They may only stay in one stage. They can also vacillate between the stages—for instance, going from denial to acceptance back to denial in one sentence. The first stage is *Denial*—the "No, not me" stage. The dynamics in the "denial" stage are revealed by the statement a man once made to his wife: "If one of us dies, I'm going to Paris." A philosopher once said, "One cannot look directly at either the sun or death," or, as Sigmund Freud concluded, "Our own death is indeed unimaginable and whenever we make an attempt to imagine it we can perceive that we really survive as spectators. Hence, the psycho-analytic school could venture the assertion that at the bottom no one believes in his own death; or to put the same thing in another way, in the unconscious, every one of us is convinced of his own immortality."

If you see or feel that the dying patient is in the stage of denial, you should not try to destroy this denial. Let the

*Elisabeth Kubler-Ross, M.D., *On Death and Dying* (New York: MacMillan Publishing Co., Inc., 1969).

patient deny if he wants to; it is filling a need. However, you should in no way enter into denial with the patient. In other words, if the patient says, "I will be out of here in a week and will be able to carry on where I left off" and you know better, don't say, "That's right! They don't know what they're doing anyway."

The second stage of dying is *Anger* or the "Why me?" stage. The dying patient may at times be very difficult to visit. He may be extremely hostile and angry. You should be aware, however, that this hostility and anger is really aimed at what is happening to the patient and not at *you*. You should never take this anger personally. You just happen to be handy for the patient to rail against. It is not uncommon to hear a patient rail out against God. That is okay. God can take it. The patient should be encouraged to vent anger, as it is a very therapeutic way to rid oneself of the turmoil that is going on inside. Anger is another way of saying, "I am lonely! Please don't leave me alone!" Unfortunately, anger has the reverse effect of what the patient really wants—it turns people away.

The third stage of dying is *Bargaining* or the "Okay, me, but . . . " stage. This stage is less well known but equally helpful to the patient, though only for brief periods of time. Some sort of agreement that may postpone the inevitable happening is sought. The patient has used denial, then anger, and now tries to bargain. Like a child when he gets upset because he can't have his way, first he is angry, then he resorts to bargaining: "If I'm good for a week and help you around the house, will you let me . . . ?" The dying patient's wish is most always an extension of life followed by the wish for a few more days without pain or physical discomfort. He may say, "I will be willing to go, right after my son gets married." Bargaining is really an attempt to postpone. It has to include a prize offered "for special behavior." It also sets a self-imposed "deadline." It usually includes an implicit promise that the patient will not ask for more if this one postponement is granted. However, most patients will not keep their promise. In the case mentioned above, after the son gets married, then it changes to "Okay, I'm ready to go, but not until my first grandchild is born." This is sort of like saying, "If I can have one more dish of ice cream, then I'll go on my diet."

Most bargains are made with God and are usually kept a secret or mentioned between the lines or in confidence with the chaplain or minister. A number of patients will promise a "life dedicated to God" or a "life in the service of the church" in exchange for some additional time.

Psychologically, promises may be associated with quiet guilt, and it would, therefore, be helpful if such remarks were not brushed aside by you. The patient may have feelings of guilt for not being as active as he thinks he should have been. The patient should be helped to be relieved of these irrational fears, to be able to accept forgiveness or be relieved of the need for punishment.

The fourth stage of dying is *Depression*, or the "Yes, me" stage. When the terminally ill patient can no longer deny his illness, when he is forced to undergo more surgery, chemotherapy, radiation, et cetera, he cannot smile, bargain, or wish it away anymore; then his numbness or stoicism, his anger and rage, his bargaining will soon be replaced with a sense of great loss. Tremendous expense, loss of home, finances, and being a burden all add to the sadness and guilt of the patient. All of these added together spell *Depression*.

There are two kinds of depression suffered by the terminally ill: reactive depression and preparatory depression. They differ tremendously in nature and should be dealt with quite differently.

Reactive depression is usually depression that is suffered from a past loss, e.g., removal of a breast, an arm, or a leg because of cancer. These patients should be helped to overcome their feelings of depression by accentuating their other features and attributes. These patients can usually be cheered up. They have many things to share and should be encouraged to do so.

Preparatory depression is usually depression that is suffered by an impending loss. These patients usually cannot be cheered up. They should not be encouraged to look at the "sunny side" of things, as this would mean that they should deny what is happening to them and that they should not contemplate their impending loss. In other words, it would only serve to reinforce denial.

The patient should be allowed to express his sorrow. By doing so, he will find a final acceptance much easier, and he will be grateful to those who can sit with him during this stage of depression without constantly telling him not to be sad. Preparatory depression is usually a silent type of depression, in contrast to reactive depression. There is usually little or no need for conversation. It is usually more of a feeling that can be mutually expressed and is often done better with a touch of the hand, stroking of the hair, an embrace, or just silently being together.

This is the time when too much interference from visitors who try to "cheer him up" hinders his emotional preparation for death rather than enhances it. The patient is beginning to separate himself from his loved ones and is preparing to die.

Preparatory depression is necessary and beneficial if the patient is to die in a stage of acceptance and peace. Only patients who have been able to work through their anguish and anxiety are able to achieve this stage. If this reassurance can be passed on by you and shared with the family and loved ones of the dying patient, they, too, can be spared much unnecessary anguish.

The fifth and final stage of dying is called *Acceptance,* or the "Okay, me," stage. If the patient has been given some help in working through the previously described stages, he will reach a stage during which he is neither depressed nor angry about his impending death. He will have been able to express his previous feelings, his envy for the living and healthy, his anger at those who do not have to face their end so soon. He will have mourned the impending loss of so many meaningful people and places, and he will contemplate his coming end with a certain degree of quiet expectation.

He will be tired and, in most cases, quite weak. He will doze off to sleep quite often, but it will be a peaceful sleep rather than the fitful rest he encountered during the times of depression. It is a gradually increasing need to extend the hours of sleep very similar to that of the newborn child but in reverse order. This is not a resigned and hopeless "giving up," a sense of "What's the use?" or "I just can't fight it any longer." However, acceptance should not be mistaken as being a happy stage. It is almost void of feelings. It is as if the pain is gone, and in many cases it is. The struggle is over and the time for final rest has come.

It is at this point—in the *Acceptance* stage—that the family usually needs more help, understanding, visits, and support than the patient himself.

While the dying patient has found some peace and acceptance, his circle of interests diminishes. He wishes to be left alone or at least not be stirred up by news and problems of the outside world. Visitors many times are not desired, and if they come, the patient is no longer in a talkative mood. He often requests limitation of the number of people and prefers short visits. The television and radio are usually off at this stage, and communications become more nonverbal than verbal. The patient may just make a gesture of the hand to invite the visitor to sit down for a while. He may just hold the visitor's hand and ask him to sit in silence. Such moments of silence may be the most meaningful communication for visitors who are not uncomfortable in the presence of a dying person.

You should let the patient know that it is all right to say nothing. The important things are taken care of, and it's only a question of time until he can close his eyes forever.

Visiting a dying patient, especially in the *Acceptance* stage, should be done, if at all possible, in the evening. This will usually lend itself to a very meaningful encounter, as it is the end of the day both for you and the patient. It is the time when the hospital's page system does not interrupt such a moment, when the nurse doesn't come in to take blood pressure and temperature, and the cleaning woman is not mopping the floor. It takes just a little time, but it is comforting for the patient to know that he is not forgotten when nothing else can be done for him. It is gratifying for you as well, as it will show you that dying is not such a frightening, horrible thing after all.

How, then, do you as a visitor know when a patient is giving up "too early" when you feel that a little more fight on the patient's part, combined with the help of the medical profession, could give him a chance to live a little longer? How do we differentiate this from the stage of *Acceptance*, when our wish to prolong life often contradicts the patient's wish to die in peace?

If you are unable to differentiate between these two stages, you will do more harm than good to the patient. You will be frustrated in your efforts and will make the patient's dying a painful last experience.

Patients who are in the stage of *Acceptance* show a very outstanding feeling of equanimity and peace. There is something very dignified about these patients, while people in the stage of *Resignation* are very often indignant, full of bitterness and anguish, and very often express their feelings by statements such as "What's the use?" or "I'm tired of fighting it." They have a feeling of futility, of uselessness, and lack of peace that is quite easily distinguishable from a genuine stage of *Acceptance*.

Listed below are some do's and don't's to follow when visiting the dying patient:

1. It is not your place to inform the patient that he has a terminal illness. This is the physician's task. (I firmly believe that a patient should be told that he has a terminal illness if he wants to know. We have no right to keep this information from the patient.) Chances are that 99 percent of the time the patient knows he is dying before the doctor does. By not telling him, it is necessary for him to use up his energy in "protecting his family from the horrible truth." Likewise, the family knows the truth, but by not letting the patient know they know, there is no conversation beyond the superfluous, no sharing of intimate feelings, no planning together. Because of this taboo, the experience of dying can be cruelly isolating, with no one daring to broach the subject to the dying person and his uneasy awareness that for him to bring it up would be to invite further isolation. Thus the patient is forced to live all alone on the brink of an abyss with no one who understands him or his problem.

A major concern of the dying is their inability to look out for themselves—the approaching reality of their inevitable helplessness. Dying is an enforced giving up, a losing of all command and control of even the slightest things. It therefore can be tremendously reassuring and helpful to the dying patient to know that someone who knows he is dying will take charge and see him through it to the end. If, on the other hand, the patient ends up with full responsibility for his own dying, he will have no recourse but helpless and useless worrying.

2. An anxious visitor will make an anxious patient. Be comfortable when visiting the dying patient or don't visit at all.

3. Be aware of pain! Touch is very valuable in visiting the dying patient, but it can also be an intrusion. Some types of diseases, especially some forms of cancer, can make the skin very sore to the touch. Be especially aware of nonverbals. The patient will very rarely tell you not to touch, for fear he will chase you away and you won't come back again. However, if he pulls his hand away from you or turns his head away from your hand, he is telling you that it hurts.

4. Do not try to "cheer up" the dying patient. This in most cases only makes him feel worse. "How can you be so cheerful when I am lying here dying?"

5. Don't talk about how beautiful the weather is. The patient may hate you for it because you can leave and go back outside and he can't.

6. Pick out greeting cards with care. Some greeting cards should be thrown in the garbage. They are far too shallow and syrupy. Do not send "Get Well" cards to a dying patient. These only make him feel worse.

7. Flowers are helpful and meaningful, but check first to see if the patient has any allergies.

8. Do not pile covers on the patient because you think he feels cold! The dying patient, in most cases, is not conscious of being cold regardless of how cold his body surface feels. If the patient is restless, it is usually because he is too warm and he is attempting to throw off the bedclothes.

9. Never pull the shades or shut off the light! There should be indirect lighting in the patient's room at all times—day or night. To the dying patient, darkness is often equated with death. In dying, the patient often reverts back to his childhood days and once again becomes afraid of the dark.

10. Never whisper in the corner or near the patient's room. The patient will be sure that you are talking about his condition regardless of what you are talking about.

11. Always answer questions honestly. If the patient asks, "Am I going to die?," you can honestly answer, "You are very seriously ill, but everything possible is being done for you."

12. Pray with the patient if you feel comfortable doing so. If you do not and the patient wishes to pray, call for the chaplain or the patient's minister. Always ask the patient first if he would like to pray with you. Don't force your beliefs upon him. Reading Scripture to the patient can be very helpful. Some favorites are: The Twenty-third Psalm, The Lord's Prayer, and Joshua 1:9.

13. Never leave the patient isolated or abandoned. Remember that loneliness is the worst fear of the dying patient. Loneliness has a profound relationship to pain—pain is always most intense when the patient is left alone.

14. Help the patient and family realize that death is as much a part of life as birth. All of us will experience it sooner or later.

15. Help to allay the feeling of meaninglessness. Try to excite the imagination. Show the patient you are concerned about him—that you care.

Help then is really needed in terms of how to live, not how to die. A person's ultimate challenge in dying is whether it has meaning or whether it is the final triumph of meaninglessness. A person can endure much more pain if it has meaning to him. The quest for meaning gives to pain and death a direction and a purpose. Therefore, one way to reduce the patient's fear of death is to rearouse his creative impulses. There is a need of the person to find meaning for his dying just as he sought meaning for his living. Your role with the patient, then, is not merely that of bringing peace but also that of bringing meaning and order to the events that are being experienced. You should try to give meaning to death in accord with the person's meaning for life, so that the act of dying is not separated from life but is rather a continuation of the mood and manner of living.

A patient may wish to live and fight for life for different reasons. The two reasons most frequently given are the fear of death and the wish to live. Clinical experience seems to indicate that in serious physical illness, the fear of death is not a very powerful tool. The wish to live, however, appears to be the much stronger weapon. In mobilizing this wish to live, we must have goals in the future that are deeply important to the patient. We need an ideal to work toward. The ideal of the full, rich self, the development of one's own being in one's own special way, the freedom to be one's self freely without fear is a goal worth fighting and suffering for.

Another way of bringing meaning to a person's life is the way that he dies, the legacy that one leaves to his loved ones. Accepting death as a part of life and truly living until one is dead gives meaning to one's dying.

An important thing for you to remember is that you should not raise false hopes. The concentration should be more on the expansion and feeling of the self than on physical recovery. The patient's image of himself appears to be an important factor in the management of disease—especially in the terminal phases. You should help the patient find a meaning in life so rich in value that he will not be overwhelmed by the biological incident related to mortality. The religious person who dies in faith and who shares his faith and devotion with his family and his community performs a most meaningful emotional service. To die in faith is a witness of God's love that brings courage and hope to the whole community.

You should try to develop the idea that people can die healthy. While the physical equipment may wear out or break down, the achievement of the full measure of self-awareness and spiritual realization makes this terminal moment not a time of defeat but a final expression of faith.

Dying persons often toward the end of life give a strenuous effort both on the conscious and unconscious levels to bring order and meaning into life, as if to end things in a neat and tidy manner.

It is the feeling of guilt more than anything else that separates a dying person from those around him, as well as from his God. Much of this guilt stems from the patient's belief that his illness is a sign of sin and death is a form of punishment. Your role is to assure him that this view is not supported by biblical teaching and it violates the whole concept of medical practice. If illness were a form of punishment, then the physician would be guilty of meddling in matters of divine judgment. If death were the final form of punishment, then there would be evidence of an indiscriminate judge at work— for all that lives dies.

People who visit and work with patients in catastrophic situations will usually find to their surprise that there are real rewards that are not first surmised or expected. One will see clearly the strength and dignity of human beings, the deep altruism, the positive qualities that exist at all levels of personality.

Visiting and working with people under the banner of fate increases one's respect for them greatly and makes one proud of being a human being. You should not be interested in the dying patient because he is dying or because he is a patient, but rather because that person is entitled to be treated as a person at all times and in all circumstances, even to the end of his allotted physical time. You should help the patient grow in his understanding of the meaning of life.

Visitors and loved ones can be the key to how well a patient manages his dying process. If they can prevent each other from retreating behind a wall of denial and can encourage each other to face the dying patient and death squarely and openly, they will go a long way toward ensuring that the patient will have the support he needs during his last journey on earth.

There are some specific problems that can occur when visiting the dying patient—especially if the dying process is over a prolonged period of time. One of the most serious problems is what might be called "the survivor syndrome." For the bereaved, ordinary feelings of sadness, grief, and loss are hard enough to bear, but at least they are natural, respectable, and understandable feelings that actually serve as a healing process. But the survivor syndrome is much different. These feelings serve no apparently useful purpose and generally are regarded as not respectable, not understandable, and not natural and can be devastating both to the patient and the visitor. Essentially, the survivor syndrome consists of anger, hostility, hate, and guilt toward the dying patient. They may even include a wish that the patient would "hurry up and die and get it over with." These feelings, of course, cause undue guilt and may very well have a strong adverse affect upon the patient's last days. When and if such reactions occur, the visitor should seek help from someone—perhaps a grief counselor with whom he can share his feelings.

Chapter Eight

VISITING CHILDREN CONFRONTED WITH DEATH

CHILDREN FOR ONE REASON OR ANOTHER usually seem to cope better than adults when it comes to death and dying. This seems to be true whether it is the child himself who is dying or whether it is a loved one who is dying. Children should grow up with a healthy attitude toward death. If they are kept from knowing about death or are told falsehoods, they tend to build up anxieties and fears about death, which in time give them an unhealthy attitude.

There are certain development processes in a child's life of which you should be aware when talking to him about death. The first stage is from birth to about three years of age. At this age, the child usually has no concept of death whatsoever. However, he does have a tremendous sense of loss and grief. When dealing with children at this age, one should give simple but honest answers to the child's questions and basic tender, loving care.

Unfortunately, we as adults and parents seem to always have to have an answer, especially to children. *Don't be afraid to say, "I don't know!"* For instance, suppose a child asks, "Is my mother in heaven with God?" No one really knows the answer to this question. However, if that is your belief, there is nothing wrong with saying, "I don't know for sure, but I certainly believe she is." This is a simple, honest answer.

The second developmental stage is from about four to seven years of age. At this age, the child is primarily concerned with exploring the meaning of his own body and his bodily functions. When he experiences a death of a loved one, he will quite naturally ask questions concerning his major area of interest. He cannot fully comprehend what deadness is all about. He will ask questions such as "Do you eat when you are dead?," "Can you see when you are dead?," and "Do you go to the bathroom when you are dead?" The visitor should give simple, honest answers. By all means do not say, "When you are dead you are just like you are asleep!" This may cause the child great fears of going to sleep. *Do not overanswer.* This only causes anxiety. Answer the questions asked with as simple an answer as possible. If the child wants to know more, he will ask.

The next stage of development is from about seven to twelve years of age. At this stage, the child will ask more significant and pertinent questions. He will be in school and with his friends so he will be more socially involved with people who have death in their families. Again, simple, honest answers are the rule.

The next stage of development is from about twelve to fifteen years of age. This is the stage where the child begins to explore the meaning of life. He can have a healthy fear of death that will help to protect life or he can have an anxious fear of death that can prove to be life-destroying. His feelings will usually be a result of how he has been exposed through the previous stages of development. If the child has a free and uncluttered mind, he can move into philosophical maturity. However, if he has been charged with anxiety through the earlier years, he can very well move into self-destructive behavior. Suicide can be an attempt, often unconscious, to control death; "death will not catch *me* unaware."

As the child moves on into adulthood, his attitudes toward death will be an accumulation of what has developed through the various previous stages. If he has been filled with anxiety and apprehension, he will carry this into adulthood and, unfortunately, will pass it along to the future generations. If, on the other hand, he has experience of the kind of openness and honesty that answers his questions in the mood and atmosphere of reassurance and love, he will arrive at the place where he values his life and protects it. He will measure every day as a gift that is to be cherished and will not engage in symbolic self-destructive behavior.

A person who visits or deals with children who are either dying or are grieving the loss of a loved one should heed the following warnings:

1. *Be aware of anxiety!* If you have anxiety about death yourself and you deal with the questions of the child, you are bound to communicate your anxiety. Usually when you try the hardest to cover up your anxiety, you communicate it the most. Therefore, if you want to talk to children about these matters, you have important homework to do. You should ask yourself the following questions: (a) How do I feel about death?; (b) How do I feel about the prospect of my own dying?; (c) How do I feel about engaging in ceremonial acting out (funerals)?; (d) How do I recall my first experiences with death?; What were the surrounding emotions as I tried to recall them? Through asking these questions, we can see if we have any blind spots, if there are any areas where traumatic events have been blotted out.

2. *Beware of deceit!* Don't give the child false information. This will tend to send him off in the wrong direction. Do not lie. The child needs open and honest answers. There is no easy way around the question of death. It is much better handled if it is confronted head on. If the child's questions are difficult and you feel the child is not prepared for the full answer, give him a simple but honest answer upon which he can build as he grows.

3. *Beware of denial!* Children want to be part of life; they want to participate in the ceremonial acting out. They want to be part of things that happen within the life of the family. Do not "farm them out" until after the funeral. When children are not allowed to be a part of the ceremonial acting out, they tend to blame themselves for what has happened: "They don't want me with them; it must have been something bad that I did."

If a child does not want to participate, he should not, by any means, be forced to. However, his not wanting to participate could be a clue to anxieties that have already been building up within him. He needs help to understand why he is anxious.

Children have no anxiety, no apprehension, about death unless it has been projected into the process by adults. In a world where there is so much violence and deceit about death—artificial death thrust upon children day in and day out through the press, television, magazines, and motion pictures—there should be some point where a child can get sincere and honest answers pertaining to the meaning of death as a human experience, not merely as a dimension of entertainment or national tragedy.

When a child grows up in an atmosphere of reassurance,

interpretation, and honest answers, he builds a foundation under his concept of death that makes it possible for him to deal with it with a healthy fear.

When a child is charged day in and day out with deceit and apprehension, the only thing left for him is to approach the whole field with intolerable anxiety, with all the tragic consequences that can entail.

As adults, we need to be very sensitive to what is going on in the minds and spirits of children. We need to be aware of what is happening inside them so that we can be part of the answer rather than part of the problem.

Children live by emotion. Emotions are their main language they employ through the early years of their lives. Damaging the emotional edge of their life by deceit, by denial, or by filling their lives with anxiety is a tragic form of child abuse. Remember, a healthy fear of death protects life; anxiety about death is life-destroying.

Chapter Nine

VISITING THE BEREAVED

PERHAPS THE MOST IMPORTANT THING you should do when
calling on the bereaved is allow them to suffer their loss; it is
their loss, a real loss, and they should have an opportunity to
grieve over it. It is known that when a person loses a loved
one through death, divorce, or any other reason, certain mental processes are set in motion—processes that only time will
solve. The period of grief and mourning is, in a real sense, a
healing period, and the processes that go on are healing ones.

When a person dies, the act of death is for him the end
of his life. For others, his family, relatives, and friends, it is
not the end of his life—at least, it is not a sudden end. Realization of the loss, acceptance, and adjustment to the loss are a
protracted and painful process in which the lost object is given
up gradually and only after a hard struggle.

There is a definite "sequence to loss" that a person must
go through *if* he is to complete the grief process in a healthy
way. This sequence is experienced in any kind of loss: losing
a pet, losing a job, divorce, moving to another location, et
cetera. But the sequence is accentuated at time of loss by
death. Unlike the bouncing around from one stage to another
in the stages of dying, the bereaved person must go through
the "sequence of loss" stages in order. Only through comple-

tion of this sequence does one complete the grief process. The sequence is not unlike the stages of dying. It is: Shock, Protest, Anxiety, Despair, Withdrawal, Search, and Resolution.

Our response when we hear that someone has died is often the simple ejaculation, "No!" Or we may say, "Why, that just can't be!" Or we suggest, "But I saw him just yesterday," meaning that since he was alive twenty-four hours ago, he must be alive now. The dead person may be talked about in the present tense, or plans for the future are made taking the deceased into account. Every effort is made to hang on to the lost one.

When somebody close to us dies, our first reaction is one of shock or denial, often called a God-given anesthetic. This reaction can be lengthy and even permanent. At the very least, it takes time for the full significance of loss to be recognized.

As the reality of loss becomes apparent, sorrow will increase. With sorrow will come feelings of guilt, hostility, anger, anxiety, and protest. All these feelings, whether or not they are socially appropriate, need to be ventilated or handled in some way that equally prevents denial. The family, friends, professionals, and/or visitors have no right to stop this expression by their cautious or premature assurances. Nothing is worse than telling the mourner, "Be brave; keep a stiff upper lip; keep a hold of yourself; don't break down now!" This does the mourner a grave injustice. A person simply must work himself through the grief process, and if it is repressed in any way, it can often lead to morbid grief.

The best therapy at this stage is to encourage the bereaved to talk about the deceased. This serves two purposes: it helps them accept the fact of death, and it usually triggers an emotional pouring out of the grief felt inwardly.

Usually reassurances to "be brave," et cetera, are primarily

52

expressed for one's own sake rather than for the sake of the bereaved. The ancient practices of wailing, beating of breasts, and tearing of garments served the individual well in getting inside hurt and frustration out in the open. In our society, we need more freedom to express ourselves. You, as a visitor, can give the bereaved encouragement and permission to do so.

Following these feelings, the bereaved finds himself in a stage of depression and then withdrawal. The event of a death has taken us out of the everyday world. The bereaved is then faced with the decision whether he is going to continue to live or whether he is going to commit suicide. The strong tendency is to commit suicide in one way or another. The bereaved is tempted to kill himself either by taking his life or becoming ruled and controlled by his memories and living in the past. The goal then is to help the bereaved accept the reality of loss and return to the world of the living, to establish new relationships and new goals.

You should help the bereaved through the time of searching for new meaning and finally resolution. You can do this by showing concern, being available, encouraging the bereaved to talk about the deceased, and helping keep the bereaved occupied. When a death occurs, the loved one experiences a variety of reactions that are symptoms of grief. Becoming familiar with these reactions will help you ascertain where the bereaved person is emotionally at a given time. There are three different kinds of reactions that will take place simultaneously. They are: physical, emotional, and behavioral.

The phsyical reaction includes: a feeling of tightness in the throat, shortness of breath, and choking; a common complaint about weariness and exhaustion; the stomach feeling hollow and food losing its taste. More than this, the bereaved often has a perceptual sense of unreality. Other people may appear to be farther away than they are, or they may appear small and dark. There is generally an intense preoccupation with the image of the deceased, sometimes to the extent of experiencing hallucinations. The bereaved will tend to identify with the deceased, to be like him, to adopt his ways, to carry out his wishes—that is, to keep the deceased in himself. There is also a heightening, a sharpening, of all memories of the deceased. The bereaved holds on to the deceased by these living reactions.

The emotions reactions include: usually sorrow over the loss; perhaps relief that prolonged agony is finished; maybe even joy in the remembrance of the quality of the deceased's life. Along with these feelings, there may be feelings of guilt and anger. The bereaved will tend to search himself for all the mistakes he made before the death occurred. "Why did I fail to . . . ?" "If only I had known . . . " "If only I could do it over again." Previous hidden feelings of guilt are let loose into consciousness, and past known guilt is increased. Guilt may very well be a result of the bereaved's hostility toward the deceased. There are almost always feelings of guilt connected with a death. Sometimes these feelings of guilt and anger will be directed at the deceased person, but more often than not they will be directed at the living—the relatives, friends, and professionals who are presumably trying to be helpful. Remember this rule: do not take these feelings personally.

Along with the physical and emotional changes, the bereaved will experience behavioral changes. He will experience a marked inability to carry on the habits of customary living. He may be active. Indeed, he often is quite restless and constantly on the search for something to do. However, there is no zest, no ambition to stay at one task for any length of time. He simply goes through the motions. Much of the daily routine intimately involved the deceased, and now it has lost all meaning. There is no motivation left for his usual patterns of behavior.

These three kinds of reactions to the loss of a loved one are typical reactions. You should be aware of where the bereaved is emotionally at any given time and try to be there with him giving him encouragement and support. Remember the rule: it is easier to talk too much than not enough! A touch of the hand, an embrace, an arm around the shoulder will let the bereaved know that he is not alone, that a concerned person is there with him.

Grief reactions can be, and often are, atypical. In such cases, which are called morbid grief reactions, there may be extreme physical reactions that can lead to such psychosomatic conditions as asthma, ulcerative colitis, and rheumatoid arthritis. Extreme guilt reactions can foster depression and suicide. Extreme hostility can prompt antisocial behavior—even murder. Extreme isolation can lead to neurosis or psychosis. It is common knowledge that death often destroys more than one person at a time. The physical, emotional, and behavioral reactions to a death in the family can be creative, destructive, or both. You, by being aware of the dynamics involved, can be of great help in good grief management. When you sense that the bereaved is displaying morbid grief reactions, you should seek professional intervention.

When visiting the bereaved, remember that all the loved ones left behind are grieving. So often children are pushed aside as if they either are not in grief or as if they can handle grief better than adults. *Don't forget the children.* In the case of a death of a child in the family, the father is also in grief. *Don't forget the father!*

One should never say to the bereaved, "I know exactly how you feel." No one knows exactly how another person feels, and this statement will only cause anger. Likewise, you shouldn't say, "Well, aren't you lucky? You're so young, you can still have another child to replace the one you have lost," or "You're still young enough to get married again," et cetera.

All of these presumably helpful statements do nothing but upset the person you are trying to console.

When someone you know has died, if at all possible, go to the home of the bereaved to offer your condolences and to help where needed. Try to refrain from calling and asking the bereaved if there is anything you can do to help—at this stage in their bereavement process, they really don't know. When you arrive at their home, look around to see what you can do to help and *then do it:* clean up the house if needed, put the coffeepot on, answer the telephone and/or door, get something started for a meal if it is close to mealtime, keep track of things brought in—whom they're from, what dishes belong to whom. This may seem like a "takeover," which in a sense it is, but the bereaved person/people will be forever grateful for your assistance.

Never say, "It is the will of God." Death is not the will of God. God may allow death, but He does not cause death. How could a bereaved person—especially a child—believe in a loving God if someone says it is God's will that his loved one has died? This subject is covered especially well in the book *The Will of God*, by Leslie D. Weatherhead. In the book he tells about a lady who is weeping in anguish over the death of her baby. In her anguish, she states, "I suppose it is the will of God, but if only the doctor had come in time he could have saved my baby." You see the confusion of thought. If the doctor had come in time, would he have been able to outwit the will of God?

Weatherhead goes on to say:

> The matter came to me most poignantly when I was in India. I was standing on the veranda of an Indian home darkened by bereavement. My Indian friend had lost his little son, the light of his eyes, in a cholera epidemic. At the far end of the veranda, his little daughter, the only

remaining child, slept in a cot covered over with a mosquito net. We paced up and down, and I tried in my clumsy way to comfort and console him. But he said, "Well, Padre, it is the will of God. That's all there is to it. It is the will of God."

Fortunately, I knew him well enough to be able to reply without being misunderstood, and I said something like this: "Supposing someone crept up the steps onto the veranda tonight, while you all slept, and deliberately put a wad of cotton soaked in cholera germ culture over your little girl's mouth as she lay in that cot there on the veranda. What would you think about that?"

"My God," he said, "What would I think about that? Nobody would do such a damnable thing. If he attempted it and I caught him, I would kill him with as little compunction as I would a snake, and throw him over the veranda. What do you mean by suggesting such a thing?"

"But, John," I said quietly, "isn't that just what you have accused God of doing when you said it was his will? Call your little boy's death the result of mass ignorance, call it mass folly, call it mass sin, if you like, call it bad drains or communal carelessness, but don't call it the will of God." Surely, we cannot identify as the will of God something for which a man would be locked up in jail or put in a criminal lunatic asylum.*

One of the most devastating of all deaths is the Sudden Infant Death Syndrome (SIDS)—better known as crib death. When this occurs, both parents desperately need help. One of the best ways to help is to be aware of what SIDS is not and to continually bring this to the parents' attention. Crib deaths account for more deaths than any other causes up to

---

*Leslie D. Weatherhead, *The Will of God* (Nashville, Tennessee: Abingdon, 1972), pp. 10–11.

three months of age and are second only to accidents in children up to fifteen months of age. There are 10,000 crib deaths each year in the United States. The following are things that should be known about crib death:

1. It is a distinctive entity—a specific disease.
2. There is frequent occurrence in all parts of the world.
3. It is not increasing; likewise, it is not decreasing.
4. Infectious disease seems to play an important role in SIDS. What that role is has not yet been explained.
5. There is a characteristic age distribution curve, with the peak being between two and three months of age.
6. Crib death occurs more frequently with premature and low–birth-weight infants.
7. It usually occurs during sleep.
8. Crib death can be diagnosed (following death) with reasonable certainty in typical cases.
9. It occurs rapidly and silently.
10. The infants are usually normal and well cared for.
11. It is not known to be genetic.
12. It is not related to bottle- or breast-feeling.
13. It cannot always be predicted or prevented. (Once a crib death has occurred in a family, chances seem to be greater that it can happen again. Monitoring devices are available that will sound an alarm if the child stops breathing.)
14. Much evidence favors an airway obstruction as the mechanism of death.
15. It is not suffocation.
16. SIDS is *nothing* the parents did or did not do to the child.

17. SIDS is more prevalent in males than females.
18. Incidence is greater among poorer people.
19. The situations are usually almost identical. There is no indication of the baby crying or yelling out.
20. Post mortems show that almost always there is water in the lungs.

There seems to be a number of contributing factors that pertain to the end result. There has been and is considerable research being done to pinpoint the cause of SIDS. Many theories have been postulated, but no definite proof of cause has yet been determined.

A most devastating statistic indicates the desperate need of help for parents of SIDS babies—85 percent of all parents of SIDS babies end up being divorced. We seem always to have to have a reason for everything that happens: the covers were too tight, the baby should have been laid down on his back rather than his stomach, you fed him too much or too little, et cetera.

Blame, guilt, remorse, grief, anger, hostility, and anxiety all contribute to marital unrest. All parents of SIDS babies should seek professional help. You, as a visitor, can be considerable help by reinforcing the twenty things listed above. You can also be considerable help by being present and being a good listener. Encourage the parents to share, talk, and rail out. Also encourage them to seek professional help from a clergyman, grief counselor, psychologist, or psychiatrist.

Chapter Ten

VISITATION AND THE FUNERAL

YOUR "DUTY" DOES NOT COME TO AN END at the death of a friend. It is extremely important to support the bereaved by attending the funeral service. However, one's "duty" does not end with the funeral service either. The days following the funeral are the hardest for the bereaved. This is the time when the bereaved are the most alone and vulnerable, with no one around for support. It is the time when depression can set in and cause a person to do rash things—even take his own life.

Funerals are for the living, not for the person in the casket. Funerals serve a very important function in good grief management. There are, however, many things you can do to help the bereaved through this trying time.

Many funeral services or cremations are planned to "make things easy" for the mourners. But is this good practice? Here we meet with a conflicting set of purposes. We recognize that there is no easy way of facing the death of one who was an important part of the structure of our lives. Death is painful to the bereaved. Perhaps it is the most devastating pain that humans can experience. Naturally, we want to ease the pain in any way we can. One way to do so is by expressing and showing compassion, patience, consideration, understanding, and kindness. But this is quite different from an effort to "make things easy" by denying strong feelings and preventing their expression.

You should never attempt to stop the mourners from expressing their grief and sorrow through weeping, moaning, and sobbing. The old admonition that "big boys don't cry" has caused more nervous disorders and complete mental break-downs among men than perhaps any other one thing. Big boys do cry, whether it is outside or inside. When it is inside, all it accomplishes is tearing a person apart from the inside out. Weeping, moaning, and sobbing are all safety valves. They are God's gift to mankind so that emotional feelings can find release instead of remaining pent up for a future explosion.

You should never attempt to mask the hurt by suggesting sedatives for the mourners. Unfortunately, in our culture we have developed the art of taking the pain out of many uncomfortable circumstances. We employ anesthetic for surgery and childbirth. We request a shot of Novocaine when we have a tooth filled or pulled. So, we have developed the assumption that we must take some form of pill or shot for relief of every painful experience or stressful occasion, including bereavement.

However, the pains that afflict our physical mechanisms are much different from those that sting and bruise and batter our minds and emotions. We cannot, and indeed should not, build byways around those pains or at least mask them for any extended period of time. Only by coping with them directly and quickly can we reduce the hurt. Nature has a wisdom of its own that helps people tolerate discomfort at a schedule the emotions set for themselves. Interfering with this natural process upsets Nature's own wisdom, creating new problems rather than solving existing ones. It has been found that masking the hurt by the use of drugs not only prolongs the agony, but actually causes the agony to be worse when finally faced.

If the hurt has been masked "until later," the person then has to face the facts by himself with no one around to give support and encouragement. Only in extreme cases, where a person is already under medical supervision for some major problem, such as heart attack, stroke, hypertension, et cetera, should sedation for grief be approved.

Alcohol is another form of sedation, except that it is usually self-administered. You should caution the bereaved to stay away from any sedatives, including alcohol. There is a temporary blotting out of pain, but in no way does it solve the problem. All that is accomplished in any case is the postponement of facing the problem. In acute grief, such postponement is unwise; it can become a chronic device to keep the bereaved from facing reality.

With alcohol, there is another aspect that needs to be considered. Alcohol is also a depressant, and one of the major emotional dangers that comes with grief is a state of depression that sometimes accompanies the acute loss. Administering or causing to be administered any form of drug that aggravates the danger of depression is unwise and emotionally dangerous.

You should encourage the bereaved to look at the body of his loved one. Viewing the body is of vital importance in coming to grips with reality. A sorrowing look into the face of death confirms the truth of what has happened—a truth that our hearts and minds desperately wish not to accept. However, viewing the body often starts the process we call wise grief management.

Many people will say, "I want to remember him the way he was!" But that is not reality! Many people have lived in fantasy land because they haven't admitted their loved one is dead.

Another way we have of denying death is terminology. No one dies anymore. He went to sleep. She passed away. He went home. She expired. He passed on. But no one died.

You should always call it what it is. The person has died. The person is dead.

What should you say and/or do at the funeral? Just being there is the most important thing. There is nothing more devastating for the bereaved than entering the church or funeral chapel and seeing only a handful of people attending the funeral of their loved one. Remember: *funerals are for the living*. Touching says far more than words. Tell the bereaved that you are sorry and then give them an embrace. This support of presence and touch is all that is needed. Remember, however, that grief does not end with the funeral service. Actually, it has just begun. The weeks and months following the services are the hardest. About four weeks after a death has occurred is when the bereaved person needs someone most. The numbness has worn off. Reality has now truly set in. This is when the person wishes to talk about what has happened. This is when you can be of untold help and assistance—just by being available and listening with a sympathetic ear.

As we said at the beginning of this book, visiting is not easy. In many cases, it absolutely drains a person physically and emotionally. But there is no greater reward on this earth than helping a fellow human being through his or her times of trial, tribulation, and crises by being present, by being a good listener, and by being concerned. That is what love for one another is all about.